Mary was eleven years old.
Her mother and father had died.
She was an orphan.

1

She needed food.
She needed clothes.
She needed somewhere
warm to live.

"She will have to work for her food and clothes," said an important man.
"We will send her to the mill," said an important lady.

They gave Mary some clothes.
They put her on a wagon which was
going past the mill.

The wagon stopped at some big gates.
The driver told Mary to walk to the mill.
It was a very long way.

Mary was cold.
She was hungry and she was frightened.

At last she arrived at the mill.
Mary fell to the ground.
"Poor child," said a woman.
"We will look after you."

Mary woke up in a room full of girls.
"Don't be frightened," said one girl.
"We are all orphans, just like you.
We make cotton in this mill."

"What's cotton?" asked Mary.
The other girls all laughed.
"You will see lots of
cotton tomorrow," said the girl.

At 6 o'clock the next morning the girls
got up and went into the mill.
It was full of big, noisy machines.

The girls worked on the machines.
Mary worked too.
She had to mend broken threads of cotton.
Then she had to pick up cotton from
the floor.

The girls worked until 7 o'clock at night.
There was no time to play.

One day Mary's finger got stuck in
the machine.
She cried and cried.

The orphans had porridge for breakfast and
bread and bacon for dinner.
They drank milk and water.
Sometimes they had a cup of tea as
a special treat.

Sunday was a special day.
Nobody worked at the mill.
All the girls went to church.
Then they were allowed to play games.

Mary was happy at last.
She had food and clothes and
new friends.
This was her new home.